A MESSAGE TO PARENTS AND TEACHERS:

Young children are full of questions. Many of their questions show a deep longing to understand themselves and the world they live in. They need help in finding some answers which enable them to feel satisfaction and joy in their present life and to lay a foundation for future learning and growing.

Most of the important questions children ask —even young children—have religious significance. They need to learn to feel a sense of trust in relation to their world and to people around them. The adults in their world—parents, teachers, neighbors —are most important in helping children develop this sense of trust. Books also make a real contribution. They can help the adult who lives with children and they can help the children themselves to come to feel the presence of God in their world and so to find a sense of security which nothing else can bring.

The *First Religious Books* for pre-school children are developed to help meet this important need of young children.

MARY ALICE JONES

Friends
Are For Loving

By Mary Alice Jones

Illustrated by Dorothy Grider

 RAND McNALLY & COMPANY · Chicago

Established 1856

TOYS ARE TO PLAY WITH

I have a red wagon. It goes when I pull it. It stops when I don't pull it.

I have a fuzzy bear. I can play with it when I want to. My fuzzy bear stays where I put it.

My red wagon and my fuzzy bear do what I want them to do.

"They are your toys," my mother said. "They are to play with."

PEOPLE ARE SPECIAL

There is a house next door to me. Sue lives there.

Sue came over to play with me. She did things for herself. She did not wait for me to tell her what to do.

When Sue went home, I said to my mother, "Sue did what she wanted to do."

My mother nodded. "Sue is not like your red wagon and your fuzzy bear," she told me. "They are toys. Sue is a person."

"What is a person?" I asked my mother.

"You are a person. I am a person. Daddy is a person. Sue is a person," my mother told me. "Persons are people. And people are special."

"How are they special?"

"People can think. And plan. And love," my mother said. "God planned it that way."

I held my fuzzy bear. "I like toys,"

I said. "They do what I want them
to do."

"Yes, it's fun to play with toys,"
my mother said. "But isn't it more
fun to play with Sue?"

PEOPLE DO THINGS
TOGETHER

I remembered. "Sue talks to me," I told my mother. "Sue ran a race with me. It's fun to play with Sue. But Sue does not do what I tell her to do."

"Not always," my mother said.

"Sue is a person. You do not always do what Sue wants you to do. You are a person."

I had not thought about that.

"Does Sue want me to do what she says?"

My mother laughed. "I think Sue is like you. Sometimes she wishes you were a fuzzy bear. So you would do what she wants you to do."

"I would not like to be a fuzzy bear," I told my mother.

"I would not like for you to be a fuzzy bear," my mother said. "I want you and Sue both to be people."

I thought about it. "When I play with toys *I* play. When I play with Sue, Sue plays, too."

"That is the way it is with people," my mother told me. "People do things together."

PEOPLE ARE FRIENDS

When people like to play together
they are friends," my daddy told me.

"Like Sue and me?" I asked.

My daddy nodded. "Being friends
is part of God's special plan for
people."

"Can't toys be friends?" I asked.

"Not the way people can. Being friends means loving each other."

"Does God want me to let Sue pull my red wagon?" I asked my daddy.

"I think God wants you to love
Sue. One way you can love Sue is to
let her help you pull your red wagon.
I think both of you will have fun."

I called to Sue. "Come to my yard. We can pull my red wagon together."

Sue came to my yard. We pulled my red wagon together. We laughed. We had fun. Then Sue went home to supper.